# Praise for *Beyond Us*

"Wow! The powerful words and beautiful images brought tears to my eyes. For anyone who has ever felt oppressed, suppressed, or silenced, the important message to be your authentic self will leave you touched, moved, and inspired. This is a must-read for all ages!"

—**Pam Garramone**, MEd, positive psychology speaker,
life coach, and founder of Thrive Now Boston

"*Beyond Us* embraces vulnerability, encourages connection, and encapsulates the beauty in celebrating our differences. It is a courageous testament to the power of moving beyond fear to a place of authenticity, kindness, and love."

—**Jeff Perrotti**, founding director of Safe Schools Program for LGBTQ Students,
Massachusetts Department of Elementary and Secondary Education

"How do we turn on the light inside of us? How do we live in a way that expresses our authentic self? From Marrakech to Mongolia, from Des Moines to Dubai, from Beijing to Borneo, people are searching for something real. In Polansky's *Beyond Us*, we're invited into a verse that celebrates the power of authenticity, its ability to bring us together, and its overwhelming victory over fear, doubt, and difference. For all ages, this book asks us to rise up from the grip of sameness and let our authentic self shine."

—**Jesse Rohde**, DO, MPH, social entrepreneur, health advocate,
and founder, president, and CEO of The Rohde Foundation

*Beyond Us*

©2019 by Aaron L. Polansky

This book is available at special discounts when purchased in quantity for use as premiums, promotions, fundraisers, or for educational use. For inquiries and details, contact the publisher at books@daveburgessconsulting.com.

For more books from Dave Burgess Consulting, Inc., visit DaveBurgessConsulting.com/dbcibooks.

Published by Dave Burgess Consulting, Inc.
San Diego, CA
DaveBurgessConsulting.com

Cover Design and Illustrations by Rin Rezendes
Editing and Interior Design by My Writers' Connection

LCCN: 2019944351
Paperback ISBN: 978-1-949595-58-1
Hardcover: 978-1-949595-59-8

First Printing: July 2019

# Beyond Us

## A True Story
## with Implications
## for All of Us

### Aaron L. Polansky

Illustrated by Rin Rezendes

# Foreword

On my first day of kindergarten, circa 1980, I stood in line at the East School in Natick, Massachusetts with my Star Wars lunchbox and new clothing, excited for what was to come. There was a girl who stood in front of me in line named Ann. She was a head taller than me and had long, straight hair. There were two boys in front of Ann, and a girl in front of them at the head of the line. As we waited for the big green doors to open, one of the boys said to the girl at the front of the line, "Hey, fatty."

I held my breath and sucked my stomach in. Once I got home, I took my shirt off and stared at myself in my parents' full length mirror. I wore my belt on the tightest loop possible and untucked my shirt at school for two weeks. My corduroys left marks on my skin. I was thin, but that didn't matter. I didn't want to be the girl at the front of the line.

Kindergarten. That's how old our children are when they learn what "mean" really means. Some learn earlier. Every day, there are students, and perhaps even adults, in our schools who deal with the anxiety of not feeling as though they're enough. Words change worlds. They start wars and end wars.

As I got older, my insecurities shifted. There were times I was grateful that my religion was something I could share voluntarily because of the cruelty and lack of acceptance I saw in the world. On a weekend in 2019, I sat at my dining room table as one of my daughters asked me for money to go shopping with her friends. She said she would return everything she bought when she got home. She just didn't want to be the girl with no money.

I immediately thought of my own struggles to fit in, and her younger sister's embarrassment about not having a cell phone as an elementary school student. Then it got deep. My thoughts shifted to students who experience racism, homophobia, transphobia, religious persecution, body shaming, and more. I quickly realized how similar we all are. I also realized that some people can disclose their deepest fears, while others don't have that option. At some point in our lives, we have all had doubts.

This book was written in an effort to encourage you to be brave and love who you are, love what you do, and help others do the same. We all have value. We all have the ability to change the world for the better. We have the opportunity to harness our passions and impact humanity for the greater good. This is not just a book. This is a passion project.

This project was created to shine a light on the gifts of an incredible student, who experienced his own struggles, in an effort to model the power of passion-based learning. The story was written about the creation of the book, before it happened. Everything that happens in our lives evolves from a thought. The book created a framework for the illustrator to plan from. This is the story of Rin, of my daughter, of me, and perhaps even you.

Put your dreams on paper. As we challenge one another to accomplish things we never thought possible, we discover our calling. Hone your gifts and share them passionately. Our work is never done. Nothing worthwhile is easy. Proudest moments are born from seeds of doubt and defined by moments of struggle.

Ask without judging. Check in—not just with students. Check in with the people who are important to you. Check in with the people who aren't (In a profession like education with no shortage of acronyms, I consider "RUOK" to be the most important four letters for educators to remember). Make time for that simple question. Sometimes the question opens the door to deeper understanding. Sometimes it saves a life. The little things make the biggest difference. Everyone does the big things.

Let's flip the classroom and shift ownership of the learning. Create curiosity and build capacity. Ask questions that start with "How" and "What" and beware of inquiry that results in "Yes" or "No." Help others find their purpose. Make sure the learning is relevant and meaningful. Know that you are loved, and remind others of their value through all of it.

If only I had known of this power (as a self-conscious six-year-old with his Star Wars lunchbox) for you, me, and all of humanity to impact the world beyond us.

"We don't change. We take the gravel and the shell and we make a pearl. And we help other people to change so they can see more kinds of beauty."

—Pink's words to her daughter Willow Sage Hart at the 2017 MTV Video Music Awards August 27, 2017 in Inglewood, California

Can I have fifty dollars
to go shopping with my friends?
I'll bring back all I've bought
once the shopping ends.

He turned and told his daughter,
"Don't go shopping to fit in."
He handed her the money.
The lesson would begin.

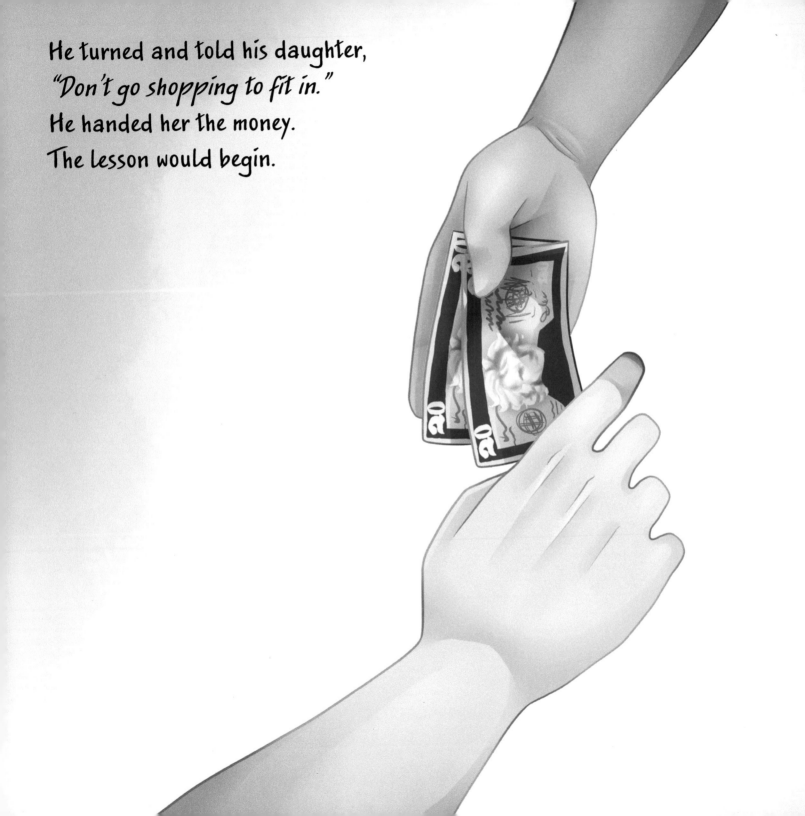

Put away your fears.
It does not make you great
if you go shopping with the shoppers
and come home really late.

We're all faced with decisions
and pressure to fit in.
Believing in yourself
is a great place to begin.

The way that you treat others
is what makes us all so proud.
Let your character and class
eliminate the doubt.

When you decide you want something,
there's nothing to return.
You give it all you've got.
You deserve all that you earn.

Don't invest in empty.
Live with passion; bring your best.
Nobody looks back
and wishes they'd done less.

His daughter, deep in thought, walked slowly up the stairs. They both took pause and realized the loneliness we share.

There's an artist in her school
who yearned to change his name,
but he worried about friendships
that might never feel the same.

And a girl who walked the hall,
afraid to show her face,
worried about whispers
of religion and her race.

The father kept a secret:
never had a Christmas tree.
Not something that he shared
for fear of authenticity.

The girl came home from shopping
and stared at Dad awhile.
"Did you buy something you love?" he asked.
The girl began to smile.

There's a boy who sits alone at school
and hides behind his hair.
I bought him brand new markers
to let him know I care.

When she stepped into the school,
she brought color back to him.
His smile broke through the wall of hair,
and friendship would begin.

The boy designed a story
with his vivid illustrations.
He shared it with the world,
which engaged in conversations.

The boy, he opened eyes
through the story that he told.
The girl from in the hallway
would grow confident and bold.

And the girl who bought the markers
brought the story to her dad.
A tear rolled down his face.
The gift he gave, that he now had.

There is power in authenticity.
Kindness always wins.
When passion finds connection,
happiness begins.

Leave things better than you found them.
Give the gift; it's not so hard.
Become what you might be.
Take quiet walks from where you are.

Love what you'll become.
Love all that you do.
Help others do the same.
The world beyond us starts with you.

Special thanks to Kathy Peterson, Graphic Communications and Design Instructor, for her ongoing feedback and support of our efforts.

## About the Illustrator

Rin Rezendes lives with his older sister Krystal, his parents, Nancy and Marty; his dogs, Milton and Mabel; and his cats, Kimchi and Minkie, in southern Massachusetts. Rin enjoys drawing, making jewelry, and baking. Rin aspires to be a comic artist, fashion model, and designer.

## About the Author

Aaron L. Polansky lives an hour south of Boston with his wife Rhonda, six children, and two dogs, where his interests include kayaking, fishing, NCAA and Olympic wrestling, food, music, and spending time with family and friends. Aaron's first book, *Dolphins in Trees*, is used as a teaching tool at the elementary levels, with leadership teams, and as bedtime magic for families throughout the country and beyond. Aaron speaks nationwide on a multitude of topics including school culture, leadership, connection, and personal development. Learn more at AuthentricitySpeaks.com. Follow Aaron on Twitter at @aaronpolansky.

CPSIA information can be obtained
at www.ICGtesting.com
Printed in the USA
BVHW092057031120
592456BV00002B/7

* 9 7 8 1 9 4 9 5 9 5 5 8 1 *